Minnie, the Talking Bird

by Jane Manners
illustrated by Chris Corr

 Harcourt

Orlando   Boston   Dallas   Chicago   San Diego

Visit *The Learning Site!*

www.harcourtschool.com

There once was a bird named Minnie.
She lived high up in the city.

She had red feathers and a bright
yellow bill.
And everyone called her pretty.

"Minnie's a pretty bird. Minnie's a pretty bird."
She could say just what she heard.
She would repeat it word for word.
That was Minnie, the talking bird.

4

It was a typical day for Minnie.
She stayed far away from the kitty.

She hopped here. She hopped there.
And everyone called her pretty.

"Minnie's a pretty bird. Minnie's a pretty bird."
She could say just what she heard.

8

She would repeat it word for word.
That was Minnie, the talking bird.

One time Minnie caused a bit of a stir.
She took the cat's toys while pretending
to purr!

10

She hid the objects far from the kitty.
Then she hopped on top and called
herself pretty.

"Minnie's a pretty bird. Minnie's a pretty bird."
She could say just what she heard.
She would repeat it word for word.
That was Minnie, the talking bird.

Minnie took more than a mouse and
some string.
She took lots and lots of shiny things.
As she removes a bracelet by its clasp,
She hops on top and hears a gasp.
14

Minnie was cornered and so confused.
She cried and cried to get some pity!
She remained behind the sofa until…
Somebody called her pretty.

"Minnie's a pretty bird. Minnie's a pretty bird."
She could say just what she heard.
She would repeat it word for word,
Because she was Minnie, the talking bird.

Think and Respond

1 Where does this story take place?

2 Where does Minnie go after she takes the bracelet?

3 What is this story mostly about?

4 What makes Minnie a different kind of pet?

5 How is Minnie like another animal you know?

6 Would you like to have a pet mynah bird? Why or why not?

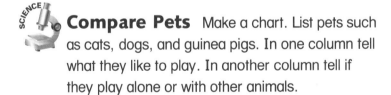

Compare Pets Make a chart. List pets such as cats, dogs, and guinea pigs. In one column tell what they like to play. In another column tell if they play alone or with other animals.

School-Home Connection Write a story about a family pet. Describe what the pet looks like. Explain how she behaves.

Word Count: 262